Better Bass With...

Rockschool

CW00549249

www.rockschool.co.uk

Welcome To Debut Bass

Welcome to the Rockschool Debut Bass pack. The book and CD contain everything needed to play bass in this grade. In the book you will find the exam scores in both standard bass notation and TAB. The accompanying CD has full stereo mixes of each tune, backing tracks to play along with for practice, tuning notes and spoken two bar count-ins to each piece. Handy tips on playing the pieces and the marking schemes can be found in the Guru's Guide on page 10. If you have any queries about this or any other Rockschool exam, please call us on **020 8332 6303**, email us at *info@rockschool.co.uk* or visit our website *www.rockschool.co.uk*. Good luck!

Entry Level Techniques In Debut

The nine Rockschool grades are divided into four levels. These levels correspond to the levels of the National Qualifications Framework (NQF). Further details about the NQF can be found at *www.qca.org.uk/NQF*. Details of all Rockschool's accredited qualifications can be found at *www.qca.org.uk/openquals*.

Debut Bass is part of the Entry Level. This Level is for players who are just starting out and who are looking to acquire the basic skills of performing.

Debut: in Debut Bass you will be concentrating on playing tunes. A player of Debut standard should be able to play up to 20 bars of music in 4/4 time, using simple first position grooves composed of whole, half and quarter notes and associated rests. The pieces very often use open strings and the grooves move mainly between adjacent strings.

The Debut Bass Exam

Players wishing to enter for a Debut Bass exam need to prepare **five** out of the six pieces contained in the book. Each piece is marked out of 20, making 100 marks available in total.

You can find more information on the Debut Bass Exam in the Guru's Guide on page 10.

Bass Notation Explained

THE MUSICAL STAVE shows pitches and rhythms and is divided by lines into bars. Pitches are named after the first seven letters of the alphabet.

TABLATURE graphically represents the bass guitar fingerboard. Each horizontal line represents a string, and each number represents a fret.

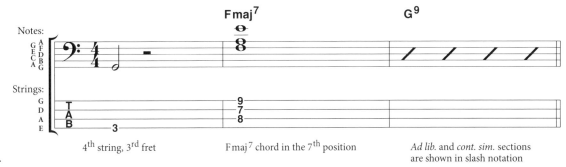

4th string, 3rd fret | Fmaj7 chord in the 7th position | *Ad lib.* and *cont. sim.* sections are shown in slash notation

Definitions For Special Bass Guitar Notation

HAMMER ON: Pick the lower note, then sound the higher note by fretting it without picking.

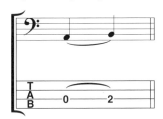

PULL OFF: Pick the higher note then sound the lower note by lifting the finger without picking.

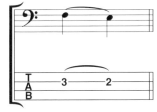

SLIDE: Pick the first note, then slide to the next with the same finger.

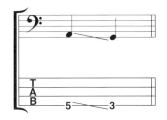

GLISSANDO: Pick the note and slide along the string in the direction indicated.

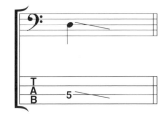

SLAP STYLE: Slap bass technique is indicated through the letters T (thumb) and P (pull).

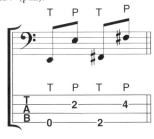

TAPPING: Sound note by tapping the string – circles denote a picking hand tap, squares a fretting hand tap.

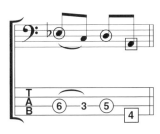

DEAD (GHOST) NOTES: Pick the string while the note is muted with the fretting hand.

NATURAL HARMONICS: Lightly touch the string above the indicated fret then pick to sound a harmonic.

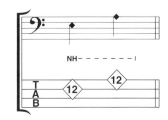

 (accent) • Accentuate note (play it louder).

 (accent) • Accentuate note with great intensity.

 (staccato) • Shorten time value of note.

 • Fermata (Pause)

D.%. al Coda

• Go back to the sign (%), then play until the bar marked **To Coda** ⊕ then skip to the section marked ⊕ **Coda**.

D.C. al Fine

• Go back to the beginning of the song and play until the bar marked **Fine** (end).

• Repeat bars between signs.

• When a repeated section has different endings, play the first ending only the first time and the second ending only the second time.

26 Candles

John Murphy

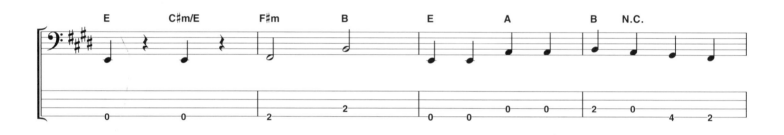

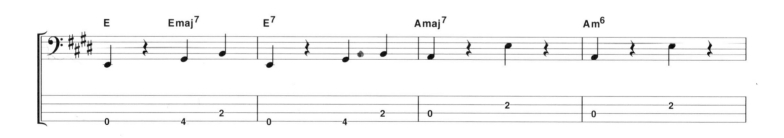

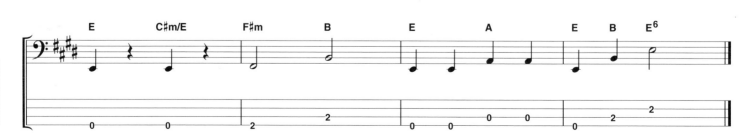

Blockbuster

Hussein Boon

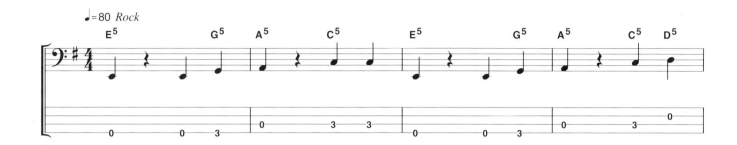

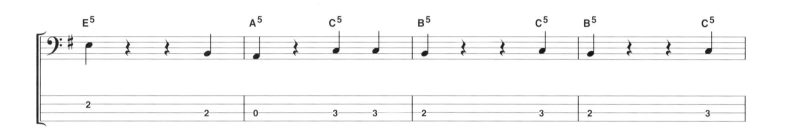

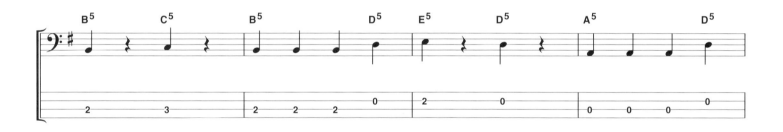

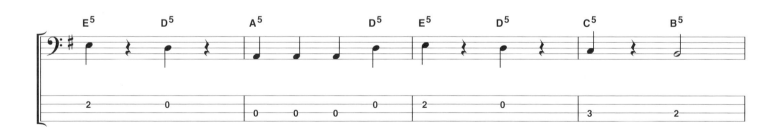

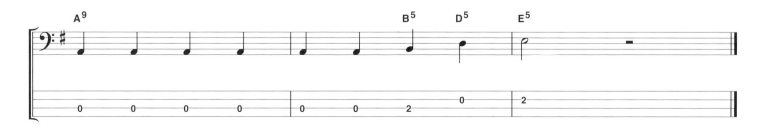

© 2006 Rock School Ltd.

This music is copyright. Photocopying is illegal.

Debut Bass

5

Funky Munky

Deirdre Cartwright

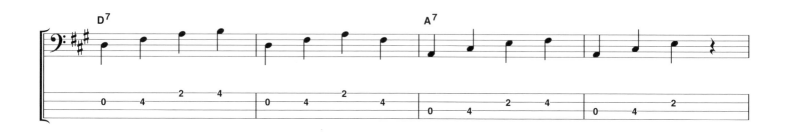

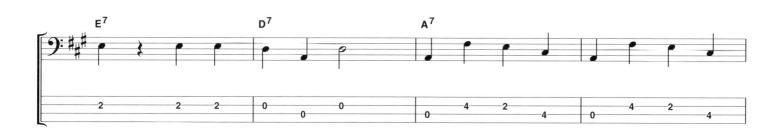

Grade Exam and Performance Certificate Entry Form

Please complete the form below in BLOCK CAPITALS. Information given below will only be used by Rockschool for exam purposes and for Rockschool news. Completed application forms should be sent, along with a cheque made payable to '**Rockschool**' for the appropriate fees, to:

Exam Entries, Rockschool, Evergreen House, 2-4 King Street, Twickenham, Middlesex, TW1 3RZ

1. Candidate's Details
Full Name (as it will appear on the certificate):
Date of Birth (DD/MM/YY)*:   Gender (M/F)*:   *This information is compulsory but will be used for statistical purposes only
Address:
Postcode:
Telephone No: Mobile No:
Email address:
☐ (Please tick) **Yes!** I would like to receive all correspondence from Rockschool via email (with the exception of certificates and mark sheets which will be posted). *Rockschool will NOT circulate your email address to any third parties.*

2. Your Examination		
Type of Exam (Grade or Performance Certificate):		Grade:
Instrument:	*If you are applying for multiple examinations, please continue below:*	
Type of Exam:	Instrument:	Grade:
Type of Exam:	Instrument:	Grade:
Period (A/B/C)*:	*Refer to our website for exam periods and closing dates*	
Preferred Town for Examination (*Refer to our website for a list of current towns with Rockschool examination centres*):		
Rockschool will endeavour to place you at your preferred town, but cannot guarantee this		
Please state any dates that are IMPOSSIBLE for you to attend*:		
It is not guaranteed that we can avoid these dates		

3. Additional information
Drum Candidates. Do you require a left-handed kit?
Will you be bringing your own kit (Grades 6,7,8 only)?   If 'no' Rockschool will provide a drum kit.
Popular Piano Candidates. Will you be bringing your own keyboard?
If 'no', Rockschool can provide either a keyboard or a piano. Please indicate which you prefer :
Special Needs Candidates. Please include a supporting letter with your application explaining your requirements.
All Candidates. If there is any additional information you consider relevant, please attach a note to your application.

4. Fees – *For current exam prices please refer to our website, **www.rockschool.co.uk** or call us on **0845 460 4747***
Fee enclosed:
Cheque Number: PLEASE WRITE CANDIDATE NAME ON BACK OF CHEQUE

Teacher's Exam Entry Form

Teachers wishing to enter **grade exams** and **performance certificates** on behalf of their students should complete the form below in BLOCK CAPITALS. Information given will only be used by Rockschool for exam purposes and for Rockschool news. You can get up to date information on examination prices from **www.rockschool.co.uk** or by ringing the Rockschool helpline on **0845 460 4747**. Completed application forms should be sent, along with a cheque made payable to '**Rockschool**' for the appropriate fees, to:

Exam Entries, Rockschool, Evergreen House, 2-4 King Street, Twickenham, Middlesex, TW1 3RZ

1. Teacher's Details	
Title (Mr/Mrs/Ms etc):	Full Name:
Address:	
	Postcode:
Telephone No:	Mobile No:
Email address:	
For school entries please include your NCN (National Centre Number):	
☐ (Please tick) **Yes!** I would like to receive all correspondence from Rockschool via email (with the exception of certificates and mark sheets which will be posted). *Rockschool will NOT circulate your email address to any third parties.*	

2. Examination Details and Fees *For grade exams, please write '**G**' and the grade number in the Grade box (e.g. **G6** for Grade 6). For performance certificates, please write '**PC**' and the grade number in the Grade box (e.g. **PC4** for Performance Certificate Grade 4). †For examination periods refer to our website. Continue on separate sheet if necessary.* FOR SPECIAL NEEDS CANDIDATES PLEASE ATTACH A SUPPORTING LETTER WITH DETAILS.

Candidate's Name (as it will appear on the certificate)	Date of Birth	Gender (M/F)	Instrument	Grade*	Period†	Fee (£)
1.	DD MM YYYY					
2.	DD MM YYYY					
3.	DD MM YYYY					
4.	DD MM YYYY					
5.	DD MM YYYY					
6.	DD MM YYYY					
7.	DD MM YYYY					
8.	DD MM YYYY					
9.	DD MM YYYY					
10.	DD MM YYYY					
11.	DD MM YYYY					
12.	DD MM YYYY					
				Total fees enclosed £		

Preferred Town for Examination (*Refer to our website for a list of current towns with Rockschool examination centres**):

*Rockschool will endeavour to place your candidates at your preferred town, but cannot guarantee this

Please list dates your candidate(s) **cannot** attend*:

*It is not guaranteed that we can avoid these dates

Band Exam Entry Form

You can enter for one of the following band exams (1 Guitar player, 1 Bass player, 1 Drummer) using Rockschool materials: *Level One (Grade 3 repertoire)* *Level Two (Grade 5 repertoire)* *Level Three (Grade 8 repertoire)*
Please complete the form below in BLOCK CAPITALS. Information given will only be used by Rockschool for exam purposes and for Rockschool news. Completed application forms should be sent, along with a cheque made payable to 'Rockschool' for the appropriate fees, to:

Exam Entries, Rockschool, Evergreen House, 2-4 King Street, Twickenham, Middlesex, TW1 3RZ

1. Band's Details
GUITARIST Full Name (as it will appear on the certificate):
Date of Birth (DD/MM/YY)*:   Gender (M/F)*:
BASSIST Full Name (as it will appear on the certificate):
Date of Birth (DD/MM/YY)*:   Gender (M/F)*:
DRUMMER Full Name (as it will appear on the certificate):
Date of Birth (DD/MM/YY)*:   Gender (M/F)*:
*This information is compulsory but will be used for statistical purposes only

2. Band's Main Contact Details
Main Contact's Name:
Address:
Postcode:
Telephone No: Mobile No:
Email address:
☐ (Please tick) Yes! I would like to receive all correspondence from Rockschool via email (with the exception of certificates and mark sheets which will be posted). Rockschool will NOT circulate your email address to any third parties.

3. Your Examination — If you are applying for multiple exams, please use a separate form for each
Exam Level (One/Two/Three):
Period (A/B/C)*:   *Refer to our website for exam periods and closing dates
Preferred Town for Examination (Refer to our website for a list of current towns with Rockschool examination centres*):
*Rockschool will endeavour to place you at your preferred town, but cannot guarantee this
Please state any dates that are IMPOSSIBLE for you to attend*:
*It is not guaranteed that we can avoid these dates
Additional Information If there is any additional information you consider relevant (e.g. band members with special needs) please attach a separate sheet explaining your requirements.

4. Fees — For current exam prices please refer to our website, www.rockschool.co.uk or call us on 0845 460 4747
Fee enclosed:
Cheque Number: PLEASE WRITE CANDIDATES' NAMES ON BACK OF CHEQUE

ROCKSCHOOL HELPLINE: 0845 460 4747
email: info@rockschool.co.uk website: www.rockschool.co.uk

ROCKSCHOOL RESOURCES

At Rockschool we recognise the importance of keeping teachers and learners up to date with developments. Below are listed the qualifications and resources on offer. If you have any questions, please contact us through the relevant email address, or phone us on **0845 460 4747**.

PERFORMANCE DIPLOMAS

Music Performance Diploma
(DipRSL Perf) at Level 4

Music Performance Licentiate
(LRSL Perf) at Level 6

The Rockschool Performance Diplomas provide flexible, vocationally relevant qualifications for experienced or skilled performers of popular music.

diplomas@rockschool.co.uk

TEACHING DIPLOMAS

Teaching Diploma
(DipRSL) at Level 4
Teaching Diploma
(LRSL) at Level 6

The Rockschool Teaching Diplomas have been devised for instrumentalists, vocalists and music technologists who would like to attain a teaching qualification without having to attend a course or write essays. The diplomas focus on the practicalities of teaching and are neither genre nor instrument specific.

diplomas@rockschool.co.uk

MUSIC PRACTITIONERS QUALIFICATIONS

Rockschool/ATM
14-19 Diploma
Compatible

These flexible, vocationally relevant popular music qualifications will provide learners with the necessary skills to develop realistic employment opportunities in the music industry.

qualifications@rockschool.co.uk

COMPANION GUIDES

Sight Reading (Grades 1-8)
Improvisation & Interpretation
(Grades 1-5)
QSPs (Grades 6-8)
Ear Tests (Grades 1-8)
GMQs (Grades 1-8)

A must for any music teacher or self-taught musician using the Rockschool grade system. Rockschool Companion Guides contain examples of the exercises you will encounter in an exam along with tips on how best to perform.

info@rockschool.co.uk

Companion Guides available for purchase through **www.musicroom.com**

GUITAR DVDS

Following DVDs available:
Grades Debut & 1
Grade 2
Grade 3

Perfect for anyone working through the Rockschool grades, Rockschool DVDs include instructional lessons on how to make the most of the pieces and technical exercises required in your exams.

info@rockschool.co.uk

DVDs available for purchase through **www.musicroom.com**

COMING SOON...REPERTOIRE BOOKS

Rockschool Repertoire Books contain popular songs from rock through to indie. **Drums Grades 1 to 3** will be available from October 2008.

info@rockschool.co.uk

Repertoire Books soon available for purchase through **www.musicroom.com**

In The Nick Of Time

Jason Woolley

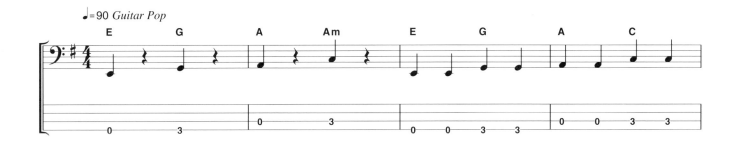

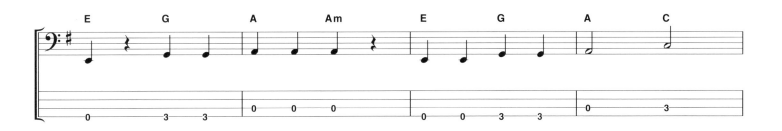

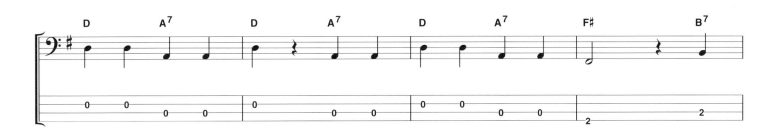

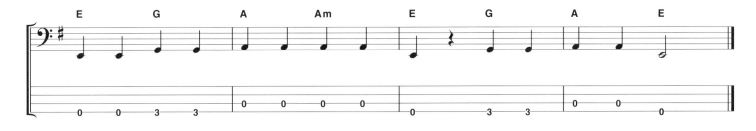

Technotronica

John Eacott

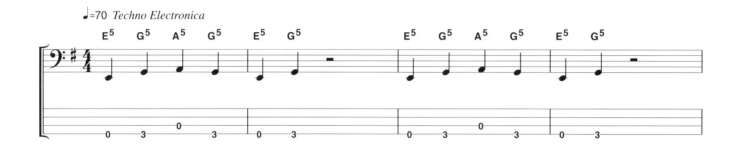

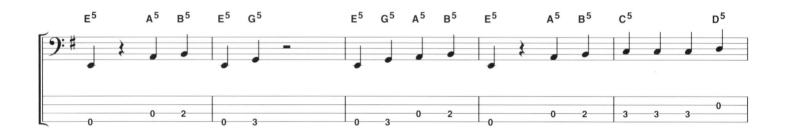

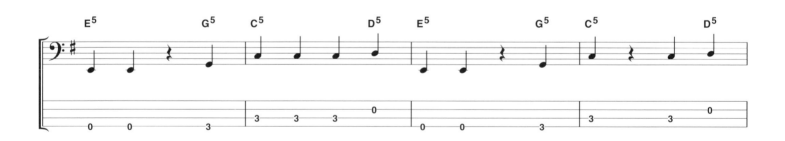

Western Stroll

Tracks 6 & 13

Alison Rayner

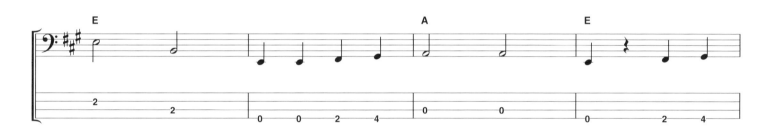

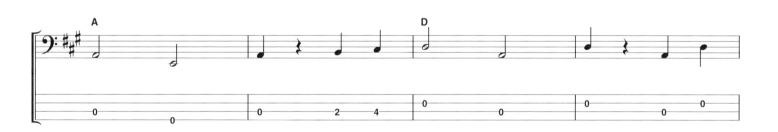

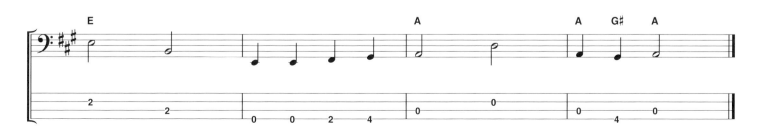

The Guru's Guide To Debut Bass

This section contains some handy hints compiled by Rockschool's Bass Guru to help you get the most out of the performance pieces. Do feel free to adapt the tunes to suit your playing style. Remember, these tunes are your chance to show your musical imagination and personality.

The TAB fingerings are suggestions only. Feel free to use different neck positions as they suit you. Please also note any solos featured in the full mixes are not meant to be indicative of the standard required for the grade.

Debut Bass Tunes

Rockschool tunes help you play the hit tunes you enjoy. The pieces have been written by top pop and rock composers and players according to style specifications drawn up by Rockschool.

The tunes printed here fall into two categories. The first category can be called the 'contemporary mainstream' and features current styles in today's charts. The second category of pieces consists of 'roots styles', those classic grooves and genres which influence every generation of performers.

CD full mix track 1, backing track 8: 26 Candles

This rock 'n' roll ballad is played for the most part in quarter and half notes. Several of the bars have quarter note rests which need careful counting. The part in the first half is repeated in the second half apart from the last bar. Watch out for the four note descending pattern in bar 8: be sure to play the part evenly.

Composer: John Murphy.

CD full mix track 2, backing track 9: Blockbuster

The bass groove in this rock track is played exclusively in quarter and half notes with associated quarter note rests. The tempo is 80 beats per minute so the part should flow evenly. The part should be played with plenty of attack and a plectrum would probably help you to get the right tone.

Composer: Hussein Boon.

CD full mix track 3, backing track 10: Funky Munky

The opening two bass notes of this blues song are played on the open A string and you need to count the second and third beats of each bar carefully. The remainder of the song features four quarter notes to each bar arranged in ascending and descending patterns. One notable feature of this song is the D♯ played at the end of bar 15. This is what is known as a 'passing note', and it creates a bluesy effect when moving from the A to the E chords.

Composer: Deirdre Cartwright.

CD full mix track 4, backing track 11: In The Nick Of Time

This guitar pop track groove is played mainly in quarter notes. The bassline is played mainly ascending which contrasts with the descending guitar melody. Again, this piece should be played very evenly, remembering to count the rests and giving the half notes in bars 8 and 12 their full value. Try to feel the bassline in two bar phrases for the first half and in four bar phrases for the second half. This will give the track a musical feeling. The volume should be kept loud and you may find this part easier to articulate with a plectrum.

Composer: Jason Woolley.

CD full mix track 5, backing track 12: Technotronica

At 70 beats per minute, this is the slowest of the songs in this set. The groove in the first six bars consists of a repeated quarter note theme using three notes - watch out for the different rhythm in bar 5. From bar 5 there are new notes added as a variation and by the end you are playing an octave range. Be careful to count all the rests.
Composer: John Eacott.

CD full mix track 6, backing track 13: Western Stroll

This country piece makes full use of half notes throughout and this gives the part a sense of space to add to the laid back feel of the song. Play close attention to the rests here and watch that you don't come in too early afterwards. The second half is a repeat of the first eight bars except for the last two bars which need to be given with confidence and careful placing of notes in the last bar.

Composer: Alison Rayner.

CD Musicians:

Guitars: Deirdre Cartwright
Bass: Henry Thomas
Drums: George Gavin
Keyboards and programming: Alastair Gavin

Debut Bass Marking Scheme

The table below shows the marking scheme for the Debut Bass exam.

ELEMENT	PASS	MERIT	DISTINCTION
Piece 1	14 out of 20	16 out of 20	18+ out of 20
Piece 2	14 out of 20	16 out of 20	18+ out of 20
Piece 3	14 out of 20	16 out of 20	18+ out of 20
Piece 4	14 out of 20	16 out of 20	18+ out of 20
Piece 5	14 out of 20	16 out of 20	18+ out of 20
Total Marks	**Pass: 70%+**	**Merit: 80%+**	**Distinction: 90%+**

Entering Rockschool Exams

Entering a Rockschool exam is easy. Please read through these instructions carefully before filling in the exam entry form. Information on current exam fees can be obtained from Rockschool by ringing 020 8332 6303 or by logging on to our website *www.rockschool.co.uk*.

- You should enter for your exam when you feel ready.

- You can enter for any one of three examination periods. These are shown below with their closing dates.

PERIOD	DURATION	CLOSING DATE
Period A	1st February to 15th March	1st December
Period B	1st May to 31st July	1st April
Period C	23rd October to 15th December	1st October

These dates will apply from 1st September 2006 until further notice

- Please complete the form giving the information required. Please fill in the type and level of exam, the instrument, along with the period and year. Finally, fill in the fee box with the appropriate amount. You can obtain up to date information on all Rockschool exam fees from the website: *www.rockschool.co.uk*. You should send this form with a cheque or postal order (payable to Rockschool Ltd) to the address shown on the order form. **Please also indicate on the form whether or not you would like to receive notification via email.**

- Applications received after the expiry of the closing date may be accepted subject to the payment of an additional fee.

- When you enter an exam you will receive from Rockschool an acknowledgement letter or email containing a copy of our exam regulations.

- Rockschool will allocate your entry to a centre and you will receive notification of the exam, showing a date, location and time as well as advice of what to bring to the centre. We endeavour to give you four weeks' notice of your exam.

- You should inform Rockschool of any cancellations or alterations to the schedule as soon as you can as it is usually not possible to transfer entries from one centre, or one period, to another without the payment of an additional fee.

- Please bring your music book and CD to the exam. You may not use photocopied music, nor the music used by someone else in another exam. The examiner will sign each book during each examination. You may be barred from taking an exam if you use someone else's music.

- You should aim to arrive for your Debut exam fifteen minutes before the time stated on the schedule.

- Each Debut exam is scheduled to last for 10 minutes. You can use a small proportion of this time to tune up and get ready.

- Two to three weeks after the exam you will receive a copy of the examiner's mark sheet. Every successful player will receive a Rockschool certificate of achievement.

Debut Bass